THOR AND HULK

Marvel Adventures Super Heroes #7

writer **Louise Simonson**

artist **Rodney Buchemi**

color artist **Guru-eFX**

letterer **Dave Sharpe**

cover art **Salva Espin, Karl Kesel & Pete Pantazis**

assistant editor **Jordan D. White**

editors **Nate Cosby & Mark Paniccia**

consulting editor **Ralph Macchio**

Marvel Adventures Super Heroes #11

writer **Louise Simonson**

penciler **Jon Buran**

inker **Jeremy Freeman**

color artist **Sotocolor**

letterer **Dave Sharpe**

cover art **Tom Grummett & Guillem Mari**

editor **Nate Cosby**

consulting editor **Ralph Macchio**

Marvel Adventures Hulk #12

writer **Paul Benjamin**

penciler **Steve Scott**

inker **Nathan Massengil**

color artist **Sotocolor's A. Street**

letterer **Dave Sharpe**

cover art **David Nakayama & Guru-eFX**

assistant editor **Jordan D. White**

editor **Mark Paniccia**

Marvel Adventures Hulk #13

writer **Peter David**

penciler **Juan Santacruz**

inker **Raul Fonts**

color artist **Angel Marin**

letterer **Dave Sharpe**

cover art **Sean Gordon Murphy & Moose Baumann**

assistant editor **Jordan D. White**

editor **Mark Paniccia**

Journey into Mystery #112

writer **Stan Lee**

penciler **Jack Kirby**

inker **Chic Stone**

letterer **Sam Rosen**

editor **Stan Lee**

Marvel Adventures Super Heroes #7

WHAKK!

Cease your *thievery*, craven varlets!

The safety of all who dwell on *Earth* is Thor's charge...

THWOK!

...and those who *threaten* that safety must answer to *me*!

WHOK!

DOCTOR DONALD BLAKE POSSESSES A MAGICAL CANE THAT TURNS HIM INTO THE ASGARDIAN GOD OF THUNDER...

THE MIGHTY THOR!

LIP SERVICE

LOUISE SIMONSON WRITER RODNEY BUCHEMI ART
GURU eFX COLOR DAVE SHARPE LETTERING ESPIN, KESEL & PANTAZIS COVER
TOM VAN CISE PRODUCTION JORDAN D. WHITE ASSISTANT EDITOR RALPH MACCHIO CONSULTING
NATHAN COSBY & MARK PANICCIA EDITORS JOE QUESADA EDITOR IN CHIEF DAN BUCKLEY PUBLISHER

THE NEXT DAY...

The *lions* are cool, Dr. Blake, but I can't wait to see the *Reptile and Amphibian House!*

Yeah? Why's *that?*

They have a *king cobra.* It's the world's most *poisonous* reptile. And a *gila monster.* And poison arrow *frogs!*

They have regular animals, too...but the *poisonous* ones are the *coolest!*

You had to *ask--*

Ooh!

What's *wrong?*

My...*lips!* For a second, it felt like a *bee* stung me.

SCHWIPPT!

SCHWIPPT!

SCHWIPPT!

The *Herpetarium* doors have *opened!*

There's been a *malfunction!* Everyone, please, walk toward the *exits!*

This happens just as we pass the enclosures of the world's most *venomous* creatures! *Not* a coincidence!

We have to *hurry!*

It's like a terrible *nightmare!*

Is it...? Jane, I--

...NOOOOO!

What--?! Who?!

Not *this!* By Odin's beard, anything but this...*

T-thor? D-did you see--?

I *thought* I saw...?

Saw *what*, Jane?

WHAP!

Marvel Adventures Super Heroes #11

Some say the world will end in *ice*... some say in *fire!* But what of *Thor?* How will *his* life end this day?

The answers I seek reveal themselves in waters stolen from the well of Mimir!

Ahh. The young frost giant *Bragmir* of the icy realm of *Jotunheim*...

...and the fire demon *Raskk* from burning *Muspelheim*.

Each holds the *weapon* I have fashioned for him alone!

Now, let them *strike!*

Let them *compass* my hated foster brother *between* them! And whether Thor *freezes* or *burns*-- let him be *no more!*

FIRE AND ICE

LOUISE SIMONSON WRITER JON BURAN PENCILER JEREMY FREEMAN - INKER
SOTOCOLOR COLORISTS DAVE SHARPE LETTERER GRUMMETT & MARI COVER
JOE SABINO PRODUCTION RALPH MACCHIO CONSULTING NATHAN COSBY EDITOR
JOE QUESADA EDITOR IN CHIEF DAN BUCKLEY PUBLISHER ALAN FINE EXECUTIVE PRODUCER

KWHAM!

Blake is *safely hidden*, lad! Now we must insure *your* safety as well!

Son of *Odin!* I, Bragmir, challenge you to *single combat!* Turn to face me... and *perish!*

I felt the hand of my foster brother *Loki* behind that *blow*, young giant...

...and see his *sorcery* in the *axe* that you wield.

No *normal* weapon can *transform* what it touches into *brittlest ice!*

Young I am, and *small!* But I am no *runt* or puling *weakling* who needs *magic* to defeat you--

LOKI is no **coward!**

You're **jealous!** Everyone knows All-Father Odin **banished** you to Earth while he kept **Loki** by his side!

Thor knew **well** the tale, for he had lived it. He remembered when Loki was brought to Asgard as an infant.

I have **rescued Loki,** son of the Frost Giant **King Laufrey** of **Jotunheim...**

...and brought him **here** to raise beside **Thor,** as my **foster son.**

A **prince** the child may be, but **frost giants** are innately **wicked.**

Loki! His very name reeks of evil.

A **runt!** King Laufrey hid him away in **shame.** What is Odin **thinking?**

Even as a child, Thor was **mighty...**

I don't **know** how the bull got free! Stand back!

...while Loki's tricks were **clever** enough to fool even **Odin.**

Thor is a **hero**—a **true son** of Odin!

Some-day you will see him for the **fool** he is...and learn **my value.**

In time, Thor earned the magic hammer *Mjolnir.*

This is your *weapon*—to wield as Asgard's *god of thunder!*

But, like his father, Thor was *strong-willed.* Influenced by Loki's whisperings, Odin began to see this as *arrogance...*

I hereby *banish* you to *Earth!* There you will remain, in the guise of *Donald Blake,* a lame human *doctor,* to learn humility.

You will no longer have *Mjolnir...*nor will you retain any *memory* of your time as a *god.*

Odin changed Thor's *circumstances,* but not who he was *inside.*

Even as a *mortal,* Thor found ways to use his powers for *good.*

Despite Loki's efforts to win Odin's *favor,* Odin began to take pride in Blake's accomplishments.

And Loki's *hatred...* and *ambition...*grew.

Surrounded... *consumed*... by the *flames* of Muspelheim!

This is more of *Loki's scheming!* He really means to *destroy* me this time!

Loki has loosed a *fire demon* against Thor...!

I now *see* his *plan!*

That *me* and this *demon* should fight *together*--

--to slay the *mighty* Thor!

SHA KK KK RAK!

Asgardians are the *enemies* of the *frost giants*...

...but *fire demons* are bane to *all* who live!

The *flames* have turned to *ice!*

And *ice* cannot *contain* the son of Odin, as you *well know.*

I *thank* you, Bragmir. But why did you come to Thor's *aid*--?

Loki *misjudged* me! He thought me so *weak*-willed and *shameless* that I would challenge you to single combat...

...then join a *demon* to fight against you.

Loki, lacking *honor,* judges others by *himself!* But it is *Thor's* honor to fight *beside* you!

Mind the demon's *whip!* He has not your *scruples* and will see *you* also as his *enemy!*

The fire demon is done?

Nay...but his form on Midgard has been destroyed. He is driven back to Muspelheim. For the moment, Loki's threat is ended.

I ask your pardon, Odinson. I thought if I became like Loki, it would bring me honor.

But Loki isn't what I thought he was. And I...have been a fool!

My foster brother is a clever trickster without honor...

And though he has fooled Odin himself, he is unworthy of the regard of a hero of Jotunheim.

Hero? You mean me--?! But...I'm no hero.

My clan is right to despise me.

Then they are fools! Come, Bragmir!

What--? Is that--?

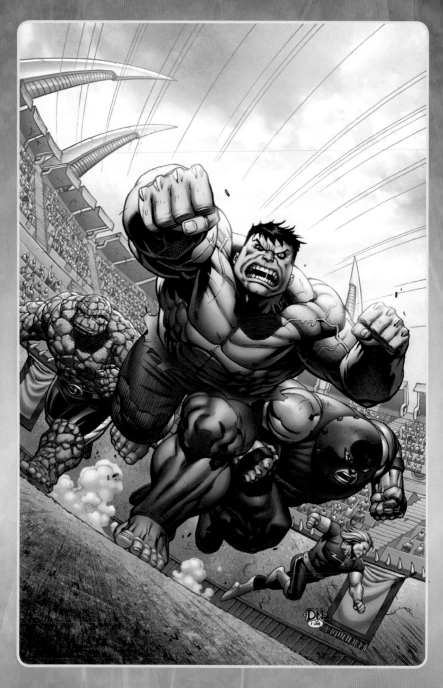

Marvel Adventures Hulk #12

You need to learn who is in charge here!

THWAP

I-I'm sorry about this!

Que...?

That's how Doc rolls! Finish 'im fast!

PLAAFF

Do I have a choice, Rick? You know what happens if my heart rate climbs too high...

Don't pop a vessel, Doc. One day you'll figure out a cure and we'll get you back into test tubes and microscopes.

"Then we won't have to hide out working these two-bit jobs."

‹Get 'im!› *

‹Show the foreigner who's in charge, boss!›

Ignore them, Bruce! Remember: the key to jujitsu is using your enemy's strength against him.

‹You shouldn't be taking sides against Mr. Cabral!›

‹Pfft. Cabral knows I've been teaching Bruce. Sometimes I think the American worries more about learning self-defense than about his job.›

*Translated from Portuguese.

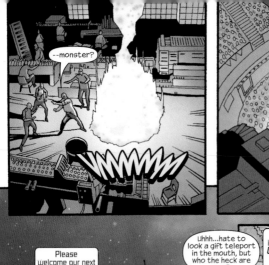

--monster?

What happened to puny man?

Please welcome our next contender!

Uhhh...hate to look a gift teleport in the mouth, but who the heck are you?

He's the unbeatable...the indomitable...the indefatigable *Champion of the Universe*-- wielder of the Infinity Gem of Power!

I've beaten down the greatest warriors of a hundred planets and I'm hungry for more!!

He's the master of a thousand fighting styles, all learned first-hand in the ring! So powerful, so fearsome, no one dares challenge him!

You're all a bunch of Spineless Ones! But I've got a new way to bring on contenders--

I'll destroy any world whose champions can't beat me!!

Dude, this guy needs to cut down on the grande mocha foam lattes.

Those holo-avatars stand in for fans of yours truly all over the universe. From the Shi'ar throneworld--

--to the shape-shifters of the great Skrull empire.

Rarr! I'm gonna get you!

No fair! Daddy said *I* could be the Earthling!

Don't turn off your viewers, folks, there's plenty more fight to come! These unbreakable cages hold more Earthers.

Like the dark, the dastardly, the unstoppable *Juggernaut!*

Lemme outta here and I'll shove that fancy forehead jewelry down blue boy's throat!

The strongman of the legendary Fantastic Four: the bombastic Ben Grimm, aka the *Thing!*

Hey, pal, think ya could quit jawin' long enough to get me a sandwich?

And that super-shrink, that psychiatrist of swat, the gamma-powered man of the hour: *Doc Samson!*

That's right! While those losers rot in their cells, I'm going to destroy their homeworld!

Hey...! Remember what Mr. Cabral said?

What? Rick, we've got to do something before that maniac annihilates the planet!

Exactly! I know how we can even things up!

Sigh...I'd hoped Earth would be more of a challenge--the Omega Cannon will make sure it never disappoints anyone else...

Wait!

Champion disqualified Hulk, but he hasn't fought Bruce Banner yet!

Have you lost your mind, Rick?!

Ha ha!

Unless you're chicken?

You mock me again, Earthling?!

We have incoming messages, your former unbeatableness.

You've been summoned to several intergalactic tribunals on charges of assault, disturbing the peace, and excessive showmanship.

Sounds like your "fans" all want a piece of you.

You win. I'll send you all back home.

That's what blue man gets for picking a fight with Hulk!

Does the FF have somewhere they can lock this thing up?

Thanks, kid. I'm surprised ya didn't try to keep it for yourself.

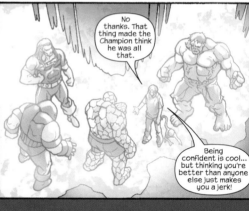

No thanks. That thing made the Champion think he was all that.

Being confident is cool... but thinking you're better than anyone else just makes you a jerk!

BACK IN PORTO VERDE, BRAZIL.

Bummer. Guess we're gonna need new jobs...

Hulk have to work?

✻ END

Marvel Adventures Hulk #13

I stand there watching, not understanding what I'm seeing. The Living Monolith crackles all over with energy. And then...

...just like that...

He's gone.

And everything's back to normal.

I don't pretend to understand it. But fortunately, later on...the Doc's able to explain it to me.

At least as best as he can.

Cosmic energy is a formidable energy, Rick. The most unpredictable in the universe.

You know all the hazards involved in controlling atomic energy? Consider that risk multiplied to an infinite degree.

From what you said...and what we saw...the Living Monolith fed off cosmic energy...used it to do whatever he wanted...

...but the Silver Surfer's entire molecular structure is *suffused* with cosmic energy.

You mean he got a massive bellyache, just like the Hulk said...?

In a manner of speaking and on an atomic level...yes.

"But then...what happened to him? Where'd he go?"

"Impossible to say, Rick. Cosmic energy is the *ultimate* in matter manipulation. He could simply have discorporated. He could have been catapulted to another dimension.

"All I'm reasonably sure of is that we'll never see him again. As far as that's concerned...

"The writing's on the wall."

END

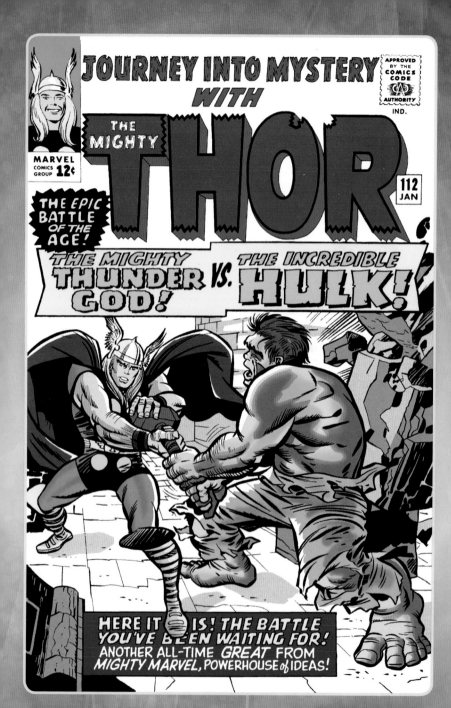

WOW-EEE! THIS IS TOO GOOD TO BE **TRUE!** IT'S **THOR** HIMSELF!!

NOW WE'LL SETTLE THIS! WE'LL ASK **HIM!**

I COULD NOT HELP OVERHEARING THE TOPIC YOU WERE DISCUSSING!

NO SENSE ASKIN' **THOR!** NATURALLY HE'LL SAY THAT **HE'S** THE STRONGEST!

I **HEARD** WHAT YOU SAID! KNOW YOU ALL THAT THE SON OF **ODIN** SPEAKS ONLY THE **TRUTH!**

S-SURE, **THOR!** NO OFFENSE MEANT... HONEST!

BUT WHAT **ABOUT** THE HULK? **IS** HE STRONGER THAN YOU ARE... OR **WHAT**??

SOMETIMES BRUTE STRENGTH ALONE IS NOT THE IMPORTANT THING!

AW, C'MON! **THAT'S** NO ANSWER! WHO'S THE **STRONGEST?**

MAYBE HE DOESN'T **WANT** TO TELL US!

NO! I **SHALL** TELL YOU! HARKEN...

THERE WAS A TIME THAT I **FOUGHT** THE HULK! PARTS OF THAT BATTLE ARE NOW IN THE PUBLIC RECORD... WHILE PARTS ARE NOT!

THAT'S **RIGHT!** I REMEMBER... IT WAS MONTHS AGO --- YOU WERE WITH THE REST OF THE **AVENGERS..!**

"**YES!** WE WERE IN A CAVE IN GIBRALTAR... PURSUING BOTH **SUB-MARINER** AND THE **HULK!**" *

CAREFUL!! THEY MUST BE WAITING... DIRECTLY AHEAD OF US!!

*SEE **AVENGERS** #3... STAN.

2.

"AND, *IRON MAN'S* WARNING WAS WELL-ADVISED! FOR, DIRECTLY *ABOVE US...*"

ONCE THEY COME CLOSER, THE HIGH, PIERCING BLAST OF THIS MODIFIED AIR RAID ALARM WILL DESTROY ANY LIVING BEINGS IT IS DIRECTED AT!!

BAH!! WHO CARES ABOUT *THAT??* I JUST WANT TO GET MY *HANDS* ON THEM!!

"BUT, LUCKILY, THE 12-FOOT TALL *GIANT-MAN* SAW THEM IN TIME...!"

YOU'RE TOO LITTLE TO BE PLAYIN' WITH SUCH DANGEROUS TOYS, FELLA!

WELL DONE, GIANT-MAN!

"AH, YES... I STILL REMEMBER IT ALL CLEARLY...!"

UGHHH!

HANG ON, PARTNER! MY TRANSISTOR-POWERED ARMOR WILL GET HIM!!

I'VE BEEN *WAITIN'* FOR A CHANCE TO GET AT *YOU!!* AND *NOW...!!*

BACK, RAMPAGING ONE! *BACK,* I SAY!

THOUGH YOU ARE *TWICE* MY SIZE, MY STRENGTH IS STILL GREATER THAN YOURS!

GOSH, THOR, MOST OF THAT WAS IN THE *PAPERS*... BUT IT'S MORE EXCITING TO HEAR IT FROM *YOU!*

BUT, WHAT HAPPENED *NEXT??* ACCORDING TO THE PAPERS, SUB-MARINER AND THE HULK JUST KINDA RAN OFF! I'LL BET THERE WAS MORE TO THE FIGHT THAN THAT!

YES! THERE WAS *MUCH* MORE! THERE WAS A BATTLE BETWEEN THE *HULK* AND *ME*... WHICH NO ONE ELSE KNEW ABOUT!

3

"IT HAPPENED AT THE HEIGHT OF THE BATTLE... WHILE MY FELLOW AVENGERS WERE TRYING TO FIND A WAY TO STOP PRINCE NAMOR WITHOUT ACTUALLY INJURING HIM! THE HULK AND I WERE ALL BUT FORGOTTEN IN THE SHADOWS ..."

"THE MINUTES TICKED BY, AS WE BOTH FOUGHT SO FURIOUSLY, WE DIDN'T REALIZE THAT WE WERE BECOMING SEPARATED FROM THE OTHERS!"

WHOOOM!

"NEVER HAD I SEEN SUCH RAGE, SUCH FURY, IN ANY LIVING BEING!! THE HULK FOUGHT LIKE A DEMON POSSESSED... ACTUALLY TEARING OFF SECTIONS OF THE CAVE WALL ITSELF IN A DESPERATE ATTEMPT TO TRAP ME!!"

I'LL SMASH YOU LIKE A WORM!! YOU CAN'T DEFEAT ME!! I'M THE HULK!! I'M THE HULK!!

SCRUNCH!

4

"YOU THINK YOUR STRENGTH IMPRESSES *ME*?? YOU ARE BUT THE HULK...YET I...I AM *THOR*...OF *ASGARD*!!"

"BY MERELY WHIRLING MY ENCHANTED HAMMER AT A CERTAIN PRESCRIBED SPEED, I CAUSED A DIMENSION DISRUPTION, MAKING IT IMPOSSIBLE FOR THE HULK TO BREAK THROUGH...!"

"CAN'T PUSH FORWARD ANY FURTHER...NO MATTER *WHAT* I DO!!"

"THEN, WITHIN MY DIMENSION DISRUPTION, A PLAN BEGAN TO TAKE SHAPE IN MY MIND...!"

"OF ALL THOSE WHO WALK THE EARTH, ONLY THE STRENGTH OF THE *HULK* SEEMS TO MATCH MY OWN!"

"NOW I SHALL *PROVE* WHICH OF US IS TRULY THE STRONGER!"

"AND SO, UTILIZING THE SECRETS OF THE ANCIENT NORSE GODS, I SENT A MESSAGE THROUGH THE INFINITE VOID...PAST THE RAINBOW BRIDGE ITSELF... TO *ASGARD*!"

"AND, NOBLE *ODIN*, ON A DISTANT HUNTING EXPEDITION, HEARD MY SUMMONS...AND MADE REPLY!!"

"WHAT DOES MY FIRST-BORN SON DESIRE OF HIS ROYAL FATHER?"

"DIRECT YOUR THOUGHTS TO *ASGARD*, GOD OF THUNDER...AND *I* SHALL HEAR THEM!"

MOST NOBLE FATHER, I CRAVE *FIVE MINUTES* DURING WHICH I MAY RETAIN MY POWER WITHOUT MY HAMMER!

FOR I WOULD TEST MY STRENGTH AGAINST A MIGHTY ENEMY IN A HAND-TO-HAND BATTLE!

SO *BE* IT, MY SON!

AND, FOR THE NEXT FIVE MINUTES, YOUR HAMMER SHALL LOSE ITS MAGICAL FORCE! YOU NOW FACE YOUR FOE MAN-TO-MAN... WITH NO ENCHANTED POWER!

THEN I HAVE NO FURTHER *NEED* OF MY MALLET!! SO, I SHALL HURL IT AWAY! IT SHALL BE MY RAW MUSCLE POWER AGAINST THAT OF THE *HULK*!

"BUT, WITH ONE INCREDIBLE LEAP, THE HULK LANDED IN FRONT OF THE FLYING HAMMER, WITH OUTSTRETCHED HANDS...!"

HAH!! AT LAST I'LL GET YOUR HAMMER AWAY FROM YOU! ONLY THE *HULK* COULD CATCH IT LIKE THIS!

I'M STRONGER THAN *EVER!* I COULDN'T LIFT YOUR HAMMER *BEFORE...* BUT NOW I *CAN!*

HE DOESN'T KNOW HE CAN LIFT IT ONLY BECAUSE ITS MAGIC POWER IS GONE FOR THE NEXT FIVE MINUTES!

AND NOW, I'LL SNAP IT IN TWO... JUST AS I CAN DO TO *YOU*... ANY TIME I *FEEL* LIKE IT!

WITHOUT ITS ENCHANT-MENT, MY MALLET *MIGHT* BE DESTROYED! I CAN'T LET THAT HAPPEN... IT WAS A GIFT FROM *ODIN*!

6.

"SEEING ME LUNGE FORWARD AT HIM MADE THE HULK FORGET ABOUT SNAPPING THE HAMMER AS HE SWUNG IT AT *ME* INSTEAD!"

GIVE ME THAT HAMMER!!

BROOM

THOUGH IT HAS NO POWER *NOW*...IT HAS BEEN AT MY SIDE THROUGH TOO MANY BATTLES FOR ME TO ALLOW IT TO BE DESTROYED!

THERE IT IS! I'VE GOT TO GET IT OUT OF THE HULK'S REACH!

"BUT, I HAD NOT COUNTED ON THE HULK'S ALMOST-MIRACULOUS ABILITY TO BOUNCE BACK FROM A FALL...!"

HOLD IT, THUNDER GOD! *YOU'RE* NOT GOIN' ANY-WHERE...!

...UNLESS *I* SEND YOU THERE!

KA-POW!

7.

"THEN, I PAUSED...TO SEE WHAT EFFECT MY BLOWS HAD UPON THE INCREDIBLE ONE...AND THAT WAS MY BIGGEST MISTAKE..."

ARGHH!

AND *STILL* HE STANDS.!!

"...FOR, IT GAVE HIM TIME ENOUGH TO REACH OUT WITH HIS ENORMOUS, CLUTCHING HANDS, UNTIL.."

I'VE *GOT* YOU, THUNDER GOD!!

I WAS A *FOOL* TO PAUSE! NOW I'M IN THE GRIP OF ONE WHO CAN CRUSH GRANITE BLOCKS WITH HIS TITANIC FINGERS!!

"WHILE, IN DISTANT ASGARD, THE MOST NOBLE *ODIN* WATCHED US WITH EVER-INCREASING INTEREST!"

MY SON FIGHTS VALIANTLY, AS AN IMMORTAL SHOULD... AGAINST A MOST AWESOME FOE!!

NEVER HAVE I SEEN HIM SO CLOSE TO DEFEAT! NEVER HAS HE FACED A MORTAL OF SUCH INCOMPREHENSIBLE POWER!

IF HE IS TO TRIUMPH, IT MUST BE *SOON!* HIS ALLOTTED FIVE MINUTES ARE RAPIDLY FLEETING... AND I MUST DO NOTHING TO AFFECT THE BATTLES FINAL OUTCOME!

11.

12

I MUST NEVER FORGET... WITH A FOE SUCH AS THE HULK, I CANNOT RELAX MY VIGIL FOR A SECOND!! THERE CAN BE NO RESPITE...NO QUARTER ASKED, NOR GIVEN!

THERE'S *GOT* BE A WAY TO SMASH YOU! AND I'LL *FIND* IT, DO YOU HEAR!?? THE *HULK* WILL *FIND* IT!

WHITTT!

I MUST *STOP* MY FLIGHT! I'LL DO IT WITH THE IMPACT OF MY OWN TWO HANDS!

"BUT, SO VIOLENT, SO THUNDEROUS WAS THE FORCE I EXERTED, THAT THE VERY ATOMIC FABRIC OF THE STONES THEMSELVES GAVE WAY, CAUSING A CHAIN REACTION WHICH AFFECTED THE ENTIRE SUBTERRANEAN TUNNEL ...!!"

BAROOOOOMM!

THE ENTIRE *TUNNEL* IS ABOUT TO CAVE IN!! I EXERTED *TOO MUCH* FORCE!!

"I SHALL ALWAYS REMEMBER THE SIGHT OF HIS FACE AT THAT MOMENT...THE DAZED, UNCOMPREHENDING LOOK...EXPRESSING SHOCK, SURPRISE, BEWILDERMENT... EVERYTHING EXCEPT... *FEAR!*"

NO! *NO!* IT CAN'T END LIKE *THIS!* I WON'T *LET* IT!! *NO!!!*

"NOR DID *I* DESIRE SUCH AN END!! IT WAS TOO INCONCLUSIVE .TOO FRUSTRATING!! FRANTICALLY I RUSHED TO THE SPOT WHERE I HAD LAST SEEN MY INCREDIBLE FOE ...!!"

I MUST *FIND* HIM! I MUST PUT AN *END* TO THIS CHARADE, ONCE AND FOREVER!

13.

"THEN, WITH A BLAZING FURY, WITH A BLIND RAGE WHICH ALMOST EQUALLED THE HULK'S, I STRUCK OUT... SHATTERING EVERYTHING IN MY PATH... DETERMINED TO *FIND* THE GREEN-SKINNED GIANT WHO CONTINUED TO DEFY ME!"

BLAM! FHOOM! KRAK!

"UNTIL, I FINALLY FOUND..." A ROUGH-HEWN HOLE BENEATH THE RUBBLE! THE HULK HAS DUG HIS WAY OUT WITH HIS OWN BARE HANDS!!

PERHAPS HE HAS NOT YET GONE TOO FAR!! THERE MAY *STILL* BE TIME TO FIND HIM!!

SCRUNCH! SKRAK!

"AND, AT THAT MOMENT..." ONLY SCANT SECONDS REMAIN! AND I CANNOT GIVE MY SON MORE TIME THAN THE AMOUNT HE REQUESTED!

I HAVE WITNESSED ENOUGH! THERE SHALL BE NO FINAL DECISION THIS DAY!

BUT, ONE GOOD PURPOSE SHALL HAVE BEEN SERVED! THE GOD OF THUNDER WILL, FROM THIS MOMENT FORTH, HAVE GREATER KNOWLEDGE OF THE MEANING OF... *HUMILITY!*

"WHILE, BACK ON EARTH, I FINALLY EMERGED FROM THE DESERTED TUNNEL, ONLY TO SEE...!"

CAN'T CONTINUE BATTLE! MUST REPAIR CHEST DEVICE! IF TRANSISTORS STOP... I'M *DOOMED!*

SUB-MARINER! ..ESCAPING!!

14.